PIANO
ACCOMPANIMENTS

for the revised edition of
The School Recorder Book One
Priestley & Fowler

by WILLIAM APPLEBY M.B.E. M.A.

and FRED FOWLER M.B.E. L.T.C.L.

E J ARNOLD & SON LIMITED LEEDS

© 1962

Contents

CHANT

Pupils' Book p. 14

Pelham Humfrey

PEASE PUDDING HOT

Pupils' Book p. 15

EUDOXIA

Pupils' Book p. 16

S. Baring Gould

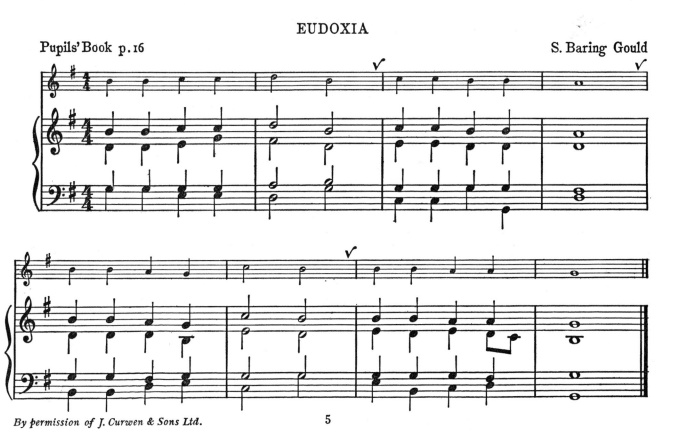

By permission of J. Curwen & Sons Ltd.

B

GO AND TELL AUNT NANCY

Pupils' Book p. 17

Collected and arranged by C.J. Sharp

THE CUCKOO

Pupils' Book p. 17

6

A GERMAN FOLK TUNE

Pupils' Book p. 17

ARNSTADT

Pupils' Book p. 20

A. Drese

Slowly

The last four bars of the above tune are not printed in the Pupils' Book, which is marked D.C. al fine

ROUND THE CLOCK

1. WAKE UP!

Pupils' Book p. 18

E.J. Stapleton, A.R.C.O.

2. BEDTIME

Pupils' Book p. 18

3. SWINGING

Not too slow

4. PLAYTIME

SOUTHWELL

Pupils' Book p. 21

Damon's Psalter

PHOEBE IN HER PETTICOAT

Pupils' Book p. 21

Collected and arranged by C.J. Sharp

TALLIS' CANON

Pupils' Book p. 23

GOOD KING WENCESLAS

Pupils' Book p. 23

13

c

AU CLAIR DE LA LUNE

Pupils' Book p. 23

This is written in a shortened form in the Pupils' Book — repeat signs being used

HOT CROSS BUNS

Pupils' Book p. 23

WATER END

G. Shaw, 1879-1943

15

DOWN IN DEMERARA

Pupils' Book p. 24

LIEBSTER JESU

Pupils' Book p. 24

16

YOUTH'S THE SEASON

This is printed in a shortened form in the Pupils' Book — with repeat signs and D.C.

THE HOLLY AND THE IVY

Pupils' Book p.26

Collected and arranged by C.J. Sharp

By permission of Novello & Co.Ltd.

ALL THROUGH THE NIGHT

Pupils' Book p.26

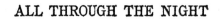

RICHMOND

Pupils' Book p. 26

THE NATIONAL ANTHEM

Pupils' Book p. 26

19

THE SANDMAN

Brahms

This is shown in a shortened form in the Pupils' Book — the first four bars are repeated

LOCH LOMOND

A GERMAN FOLK TUNE

Pupils' Book p.27

A WELSH MELODY

Pupils' Book p.29

THE NEIGHBOURS

Pupils' Book p.29

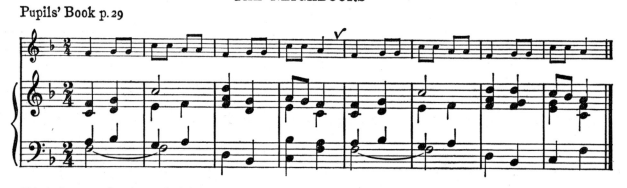

This is shown as four bars repeated in the Pupils' Book

PASSION CHORALE

Pupils' Book p.29

THE FLOWERS OF THE FOREST

Pupils' Book p.29

ANDULKO

Pupils' Book p. 29

This tune is given in a shortened form in the Pupils' Book — with repeat signs

MONKLAND

Pupils' Book p.31

DARWALL'S 148th

Pupils' Book p.31

BAMBERG

(17th century melody, slightly adapted and harmonized
by Ralph Vaughan Williams 1872 - 1958)

Pupils' Book p. 31

JACK AND JILL

Pupils' Book p. 31

26

THE HARP THAT ONCE THROUGH TARA'S HALLS

Pupils' Book p.32

CADER IDRIS

A GERMAN TUNE

29

ST. FLAVIAN

Pupils' Book p.33

WINCHESTER OLD

Pupils' Book p.34

CRADLE SONG

Pupils' Book p. 34

W. J. Kirkpatrick

COVENTRY CAROL

Pupils' Book p. 34

FRERE JACQUES

Pupils' Book p. 34

I SAW THREE SHIPS

Pupils' Book p. 34

CUCKOO

Austrian Folk Song

Reprinted by permission of the Assoc. for Childhood Educ. International
3615, Wisconsin Avenue, N.W. Washington 16, D.C. From 'Songs Children Like', "Cuckoo P.11"

WILL YE NO' COME BACK AGAIN?

Pupils' Book p. 36

LULLABY

Brahms

The two bars of pianoforte introduction are not shown in the Pupils' Book

35

EARLY ONE MORNING

Pupils' Book p.36

GODDESSES

Pupils' Book p.36

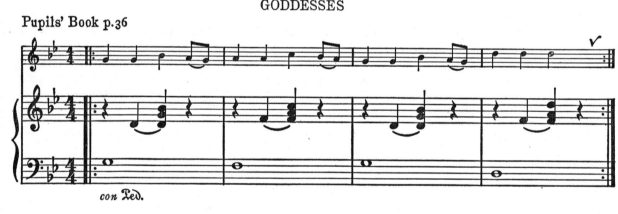

con Ped.

THE FROG AND THE CROW

SOLDIERS' MARCH

Schumann

THE SCHOOL RECORDER BOOKS

REVISED EDITION

by EDMUND PRIESTLEY

and FRED FOWLER

Parts 1 and 2

After more than twenty years, during which over one and a half million copies of *The School Recorder Books* have been sold, it has been decided to modernise these books in both appearance and content.

As it is quite common today to find excellent recorder playing in Infants' schools, the initial stages of playing have been modified so that they are equally suitable for Infants, Juniors, Secondary school children or adult beginners.

Parts 1 and 2 follow the same order as before. Part 1 is confined to the beginnings and development of the playing of the descant recorder, with plenty of well-known hymns, national tunes and classical pieces for practice. Part 2 continues the study of the descant recorder and this is followed by a well-graded study of playing the treble instrument. There are also notes on the tenor and bass recorders.

Printed by E J ARNOLD & SON LIMITED LEEDS